CAPTAIN MACK

and the
Abominable
Snow Monster

John Lomas-Bullivant

Chief Engineer Samson

Abominable Snow Monster

Captain Mack

Tracy Trickster

The Mayor

Marty Meddler

Dr Kwack

Rosie Raucous

Peter Patent

Daisy Digger

First published 2011 by Walker Books Ltd
87 Vauxhall Walk, London SE11 5HJ

2 4 6 8 10 9 7 5 3 1

Text copyright © 2011 John Lomas-Bullivant
Illustrations copyright © 2011 Walker Books Ltd

Design and illustrations by Dynamo Ltd

The right of John Lomas-Bullivant to be identified as author
of this work has been asserted by him in accordance with the
Copyright, Designs and Patents Act 1988

This book has been typeset in Kronica Regular

Printed and bound in China

British Library Cataloguing in Publication Data:
a catalogue record for this book is available from the British Library

ISBN 978-1-4063-2365-8

www.walker.co.uk

www.captainmack.co.uk

You don't want to wake up the sleeping Snow Monster!